HOLIDAY EXTRAS

AGES 5-7
KEY STAGE 1

At the beach

Contents

At the beach

Look and find

 How many?

mussels

starfish

pairs of sunglasses

Write things you can see in the picture beginning with s.

_____

_____

_____

_____

_____

_____

_____

_____

_____

_____

_____

sandcastles   **ships**

Shells

Try saying this tongue-twister several times, as quickly as possible.

She sells sea shells on the sea shore.

Write the words that begin with 'sh' in the shell.
Write the words that end with 'sh' in the fish.

ship	cash	flash	sheep	shop

shock	brush	shut	dish	crash	shed

wish	shy	rush

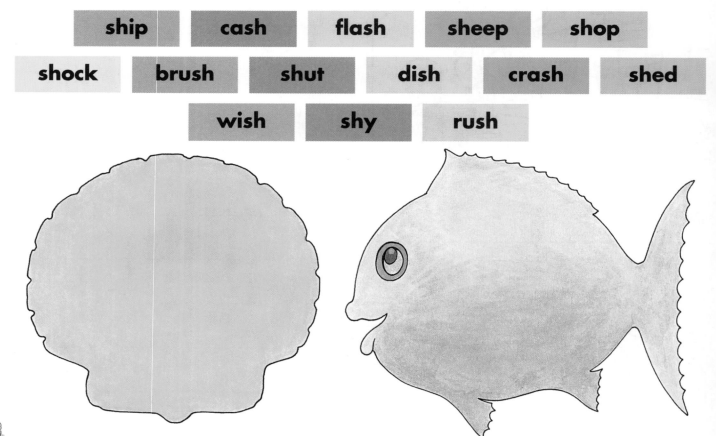

Complete these number patterns.

| 2 | 4 | 6 | 8 | | | | | | |

| 5 | 10 | 15 | 20 | | | | | | | |

| 20 | 19 | 18 | 17 | | | | | | | |

Write the missing numbers in these sums.

4 + ⬡ = 9   ⬤ + 3 = 5   7 + ⬤ = 10

6 + 4 = ⬡   2 + 🐚 = 8   🐚 + 5 = 11

⬤ + 6 = 12   9 + ⬡ = 12   5 + 7 = 🐚

? Find some more tongue-twisters to say, like 'red lorry, yellow lorry' – or try making some up yourself.

! Shellfish have been on this planet for about 570 million years! That's long before even the dinosaurs were around!

Catch a word in the pool to go with each word in the net and make a longer word, e.g., rock + pool = rockpool.

star   sea
life
sun   rock
sand   foot
light

shine   castle

house   fish

side   print   pool

boat

Write the words you make here:

---------------------------------   ---------------------------------

---------------------------------   ---------------------------------

---------------------------------   ---------------------------------

---------------------------------   ---------------------------------

Sea anemones are not really flowers – they are animals! Their 'petals' are stinging tentacles to catch prey.

Complete this chart by counting
the creatures in the rockpool.
The first is done for you.

		Total
⭐	TH̶L̶ I	6
🦀		
🐟		
🐚		
🦪		

Join together the matching pairs.

? The most popular seaside sweet is rock. The name of the place is printed on it at either end – or does it go right through the rock? Find out.

why aren't elephants allowed on beaches?

They can't keep their trunks up!

Label each snack.

Hamburgers get their name from the town in Germany where they were invented – Hamburg.

| ice-cream | candy floss | pancake | doughnut |
| sandwich | toffee apple | fish and chips | pizza |

- - - - - - - - - - - - - - - - - -

- - - - - - - - - - - - - - - - - -

Write the name of each snack in the correct column.

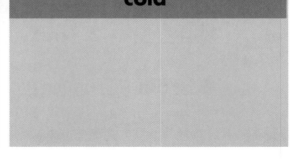

hot	cold

big dipper

big wheel

ghost train

bouncy castle

space rockets

dodgems

roundabout

pirate ship

Which words contain the following small words?

1. heel ___wheel___   2. out _____   3. dip _____

4. rain _____   5. cast _____

6. rock _____   7. ate _____   8. gem _____

 Find the names of 3 funfair rides.

 Write the missing numbers and use the big wheel code to find the letters.

The big wheel numbers: 1, 2, 3, 4, 5, 6, 7, 8, 9, 10, 11, 12, 13, 14, 15, 16

Letters on wheel: g, r, a, o, s, e, h, l, t, d, u, n, i, m, c, b

7 + [7] = 14   [7] [g]

10 ÷ 2 = ☐   ☐ ☐

20 - ☐ = 10   ☐ ☐

☐ + 3 = 9   ☐ ☐

2 x 2 = ☐   ☐ ☐

☐ + 5 = 9   ☐ ☐

3 + ☐ = 11   ☐ ☐

☐ + 6 = 15   ☐ ☐

12 ÷ 6 = ☐   ☐ ☐

6 + ☐ = 20   ☐ ☐

6 + 7 = ☐   ☐ ☐

16 - ☐ = 6   ☐ ☐

☐ - 4 = 9   ☐ ☐

3 + 4 = ☐   ☐ ☐

☐ - 8 = 3   ☐ ☐

3 x 5 = ☐   ☐ ☐

8 + ☐ = 14   ☐ ☐

6 + 2 = ☐   ☐ ☐

5 + 5 = ☐   ☐ ☐

4 + ☐ = 7   ☐ ☐

7 + 7 = ☐   ☐ ☐

☐ + 1 = 14   ☐ ☐

☐ + 1 = 10   ☐ ☐

10 + 6 = ☐   ☐ ☐

1 + ☐ = 11   ☐ ☐

2 + ☐ = 5   ☐ ☐

☐ + 3 = 7   ☐ ☐

11

The first two letters of each word are buried.
Choose either cr, gr or tr to begin each word.

Write the words you make in the correct boxes.

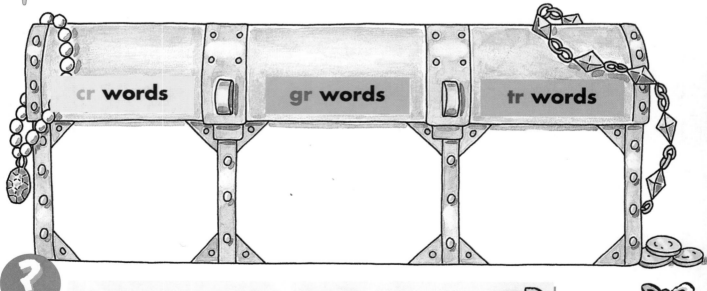

cr words	gr words	tr words

Make up the names of some pirates. Here are a few to start:
Captain Bones, Peg Leg Pete, Long John Silver.

The pirate's treasure is at E6. Mark the spot with a ✗.

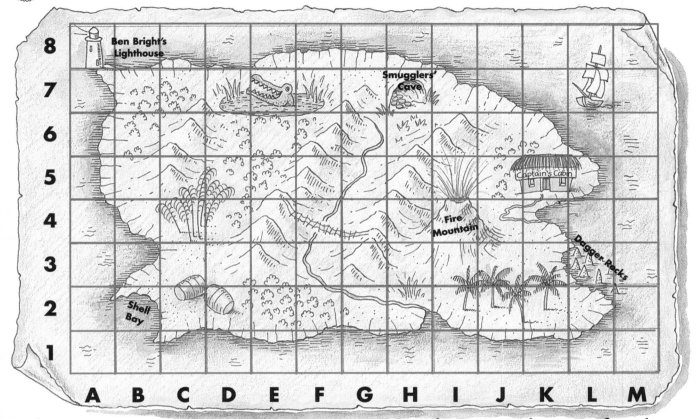

8 | Ben Bright's Lighthouse
7 | Smugglers' Cave
6 |
5 | Captain's Cabin
4 | Fire Mountain
3 | Dagger Rocks
2 | Shell Bay
1 |

A B C D E F G H I J K L M

What is at:

B 2	Shell Bay
E 7	
L 3	
I 4	

Write the co-ordinates for these:

	A	8

13

Look carefully at the picture. Tick the correct boxes below.

I can see someone ...

		True	False			True	False
1.	... sleeping	☐	☐	6.	... paddling	☐	☐
2.	... reading	☐	☐	7.	... digging	☐	☐
3.	... hopping	☐	☐	8.	... jumping	☐	☐
4.	... swimming	☐	☐	9.	... fishing	☐	☐
5.	... sailing	☐	☐	10.	... catching	☐	☐

	True	False			True	False
11. ... diving	☐	☐	16. ... hiding		☐	☐
12. ... flying a kite	☐	☐	17. ... batting		☐	☐
13. ... kicking a ball	☐	☐	18. ... riding a donkey		☐	☐
14. ... sun bathing	☐	☐	19. ... knitting		☐	☐
15. ... water ski-ing	☐	☐	20. ... building a sandcastle		☐	☐

Helter skelter

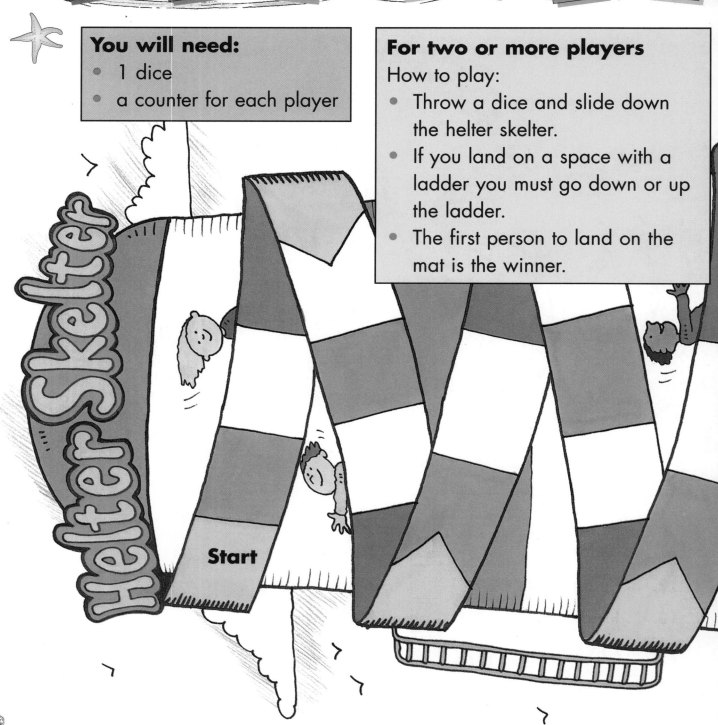

You will need:
- 1 dice
- a counter for each player

For two or more players

How to play:
- Throw a dice and slide down the helter skelter.
- If you land on a space with a ladder you must go down or up the ladder.
- The first person to land on the mat is the winner.

Start

Boats

 How many triangles are there on each boat?

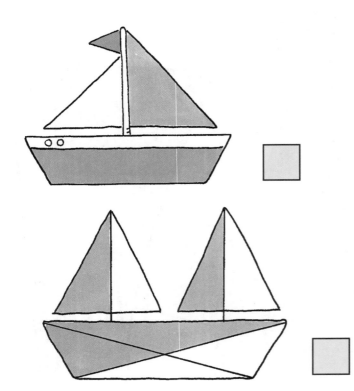

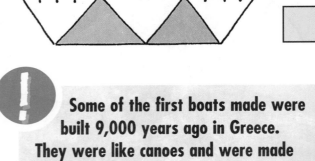

> Some of the first boats made were
> built 9,000 years ago in Greece.
> They were like canoes and were made
> from hollowed-out tree trunks.

Continue these patterns.

Think of some suitable words to finish the rhyme. Have fun saying it!

Row, row, row your boat
Gently out to sea.
If you see a big blue whale
Give it a cup of _____

Row, row, row your boat
Gently over the wave.
If you see a hairy monster,
Try to be very _____

Row, row, row your boat
Gently down the stream.
If you see a pirate ghost,
Close your eyes and _____

Row, row, row your boat
Gently to the shore.
If you see a fish asleep,
Ask it not to _____

? Look out for these boats at the seaside. Tick the box when you see each boat.

- ☐ sailboard
- ☐ dinghy
- ☐ kayak
- ☐ rowing boat
- ☐ motor boat

 Find and circle the name of each type of ship.

ferry

mhgbferryrst

yacht

qrstvwyachtx

liner

abcdeflinergh

lifeboat

yzblifeboatghi

tanker

jktankerlmnop

submarine

klmnsubmarine

 Fill in the names of the missing ships:

1. A _____ is a ship that travels underwater.
2. A _____ carries people and vehicles.
3. A _____ is used to rescue people.
4. A _____ is a large ship which carries many people.
5. A _____ is a sailing ship.
6. A _____ carries liquids like oil and petrol.

Measure the length of each ship with a ruler.

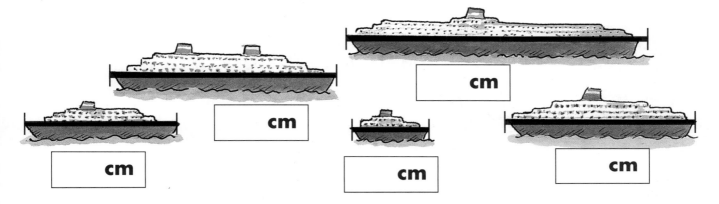

cm

cm

cm

cm

Match each of these anchors to the correct ship above.

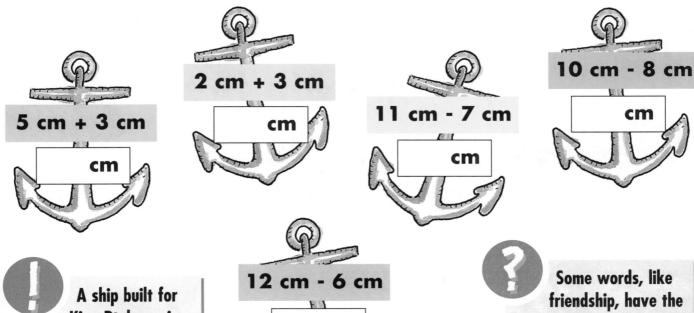

5 cm + 3 cm

cm

2 cm + 3 cm

cm

11 cm - 7 cm

cm

10 cm - 8 cm

cm

12 cm - 6 cm

cm

! A ship built for King Ptolemy, in 210 BC, had space for 4,000 rowers!

? Some words, like friendship, have the word 'ship' in them. Can you think of any more 'ship' words?

Which of these things would you take to the beach?

book

sunglasses

scarf

bucket and spade

sun hat

net

t-shirt

swimming trunks

torch

gloves

slippers

towel

goggles

suntan lotion

shorts

List of things to take to the beach

r the beach

Complete the drawing of each of these items.

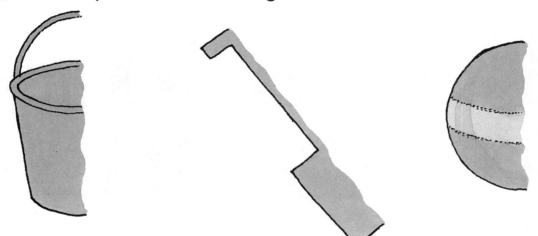

Draw the missing parts on each of these.

! The sun's rays can be very harmful to your skin. Always remember not to stay in sunlight for too long. Protect your body by putting on sun tan lotion. Don't forget to wear your hat too, to protect your head!

Rescue

 Imagine this is what you saw at the seaside.

 Write a report on what happened.

1. A boy was stuck on a cliff.
2.
3.
4.
5.
6.

24

Write the total in the middle of each lifebuoy.

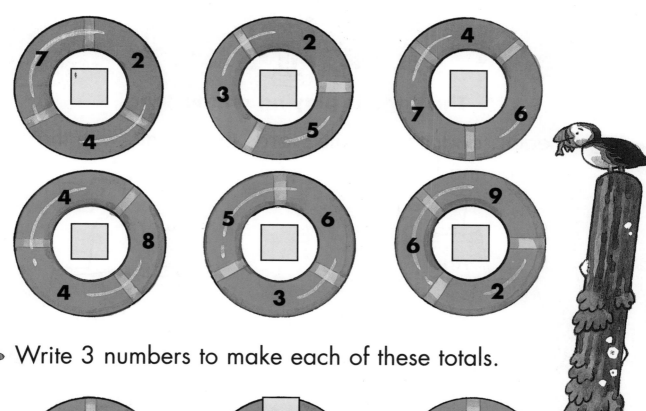

7 2 4

2 3 5

4 7 6

4 8 4

5 6 3

9 6 2

Write 3 numbers to make each of these totals.

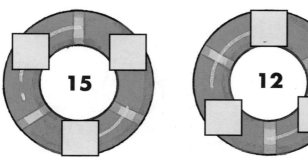

15

12

14

If you saw an accident at sea, what would you do?
How would you call the emergency services?

What do mermaids like to eat
on their toast? Mermalade!

The <u>band</u> is playing on the <u>sand</u>.

In each sandcastle, write words that rhyme with the word on the flag.

sand

band

net

shell

hat

What happened to the chicken that stayed in the sun too long?

It got fried!

Name the countries of the flags on the sandcastles. ⟶

Sandcastle totals.

The sum of two sandcastles is written in the sandcastle above.

7
4   3

Write the missing numbers on the sandcastles.

6   5

2   8

4   5

6   7

Now try these:

18
5   13
2   3   9   4

4   6   1   5

5   3   4   4

Holiday snaps

 Draw what you think Shireen did on Saturday and Sunday.

Monday	Tuesday	Wednesday	Thursday	Friday

Saturday	Sunday

 Fill in Shireen's diary.

On Monday I went out in a boat with my dad.

On Tuesday _____

On Wednesday _____

On Thursday _____

On Friday _____

On Saturday _____

On Sunday _____

Write the times on each clock.

At 9 o'clock we left home.

We got to the beach at quarter to ten.

At half past 10 we went swimming.

At twelve o'clock we had lunch.

At quarter past one we built sandcastles.

The donkey rides started at two o'clock.

At half past 2 we bought ice-cream.

At quarter past four we left the beach to go home.

Answers

P2&3 At the beach

page 2 Answers

2 mussels, 3 starfish, 3 pairs of sunglasses, 3 sandcastles, 2 ships.

page 3 Answers

Here are some things beginning with s: sea, sand, sun, ships, sails, swimmers, spades, sandcastles, sunglasses, shells, starfish, stones, sun-cream, shirts, sandals, sandwiches, sunshades.

You can play 'I spy' anywhere! Play it on a car journey, at the shops, on the way to school or at home.

P4&5 Shells

page 4 Answers

words like shell: ship, sheep, shop, shock, shut, shed, shy
words like fish: cash, flash, brush, dish, crash, wish, rush

Have a 'sh' word hunt. Look in books for more words containing 'sh'.

page 5 Answers

1. 10, 12, 14, 16, 18, 20
    25, 30, 35, 40, 45, 50
    16, 15, 14, 13, 12, 11
2. 5, 2, 3
    10, 6, 6
    6, 3, 12

Help your child to count in patterns. Count forwards and back-wards in 2s, 5s and 10s from different starting numbers.

P6&7 Rockpools

page 6 Answers

starfish, seaside, sunshine, rockpool, sandcastle, footprint, lighthouse, lifeboat.

Look for more compound words (words made up from two smaller words) in books.

page 7 Answers

Check your child's answers.

Cross off the items as you complete the chart. Make your own chart of birds in the park.

P8&9 Seaside snacks

page 8 Answers

bread and butter; salt and pepper; pen and paper; bucket and spade; cup and saucer; knife and fork; ball and bat.

page 9 Answers

1. pizza, toffee apple, doughnut, sandwich, fish and chips, candy floss, pancake, ice-cream.
2. hot snacks: pizza, fish and chips, pancake.
    cold snacks: toffee apple, sandwich, ice-cream, doughnut, candy floss.

Think of other snacks you might find at the seaside. List the things as sweet or savoury.

P10&11 All the fun of the fair

page 10 Answers

heel – big wheel, out – roundabout, dip – big dipper, rain – ghost train, cast – bouncy castle, rock – space rockets, ate – pirate ship, gem – dodgems.

Have fun looking for smaller words 'hiding' inside longer words.

page 11 Answers

ghost train, dodgems, roundabout.

Use the code wheel to make your own questions for 'rollercoaster'.

P12&13 Buried treasure

page 12 Answers

cr words: crack, crash, crunch, crisp
gr words: grass, gruff, grunt, green
tr words: trick, trickle, treasure, trunk

Make up your own treasure hunt at home. Leave a trail of written clues for your child to follow.

page 13 Answers

1. E7 = crocodile
    L3 = Dagger Rocks
    I4 = Fire Mountain
2. H7, F4, K5

Always read the letters across first and then the numbers at the side.

P14&15 Games on the beach

pages 14&15 Answers

True: sleeping, reading, hopping, swimming, sailing, paddling, jumping, fishing, catching, diving, flying a kite, sun bathing, water ski-ing, hiding, riding a donkey, knitting, building a sandcastle.
False: digging, kicking a ball, batting.

Ask your child to think about other things that he or she could do on a beach.

P16&17 Helter skelter

Check your child's counting.

P18&19 Boats

page 18 Answers

3, 9, 14

Check your child's answers.

When counting triangles, remember that one large triangle may be divided into two smaller triangles. This makes a total of three triangles.

page 19 Answers

Many answers possible, such as tea, brave, scream, snore.

Have fun with well-known nursery rhymes – try substituting your own words, e.g., 'Humpty Dumpty sat on a chair, Humpty Dumpty had pink hair!'

P20&21 Ships

page 20 Answers

liner, tanker, yacht, lifeboat, submarine.
submarine, ferry, lifeboat, liner, yacht, tanker.

Get your child to think of the names of as many other types of boats or ships as possible. What are they used for?

page 21 Answers

1.   6 cm, 8 cm, 4 cm, 2 cm, 5 cm
2.   8 cm, 5 cm, 4 cm, 2 cm, 6 cm

Check that your child has measured correctly.
Get your child to measure the length of small items such as pencils, teaspoons, leaves and small toys. Label them and lay them in order.

P22&23 Getting ready for the beach

page 22 Answers

Check your child's answers.

List of possible things to take to the beach: book, sunglasses, bucket and spade, t-shirt, sun hat, swimming trunks, shorts, suntan lotion, goggles, towel, net.

Encourage your child to help you make lists at home.

page 23 Answers

Check your child's drawings.
Place a few items under a towel and slowly show a small part of an item. Who can name the item first?

P24&25 Rescue

page 24 Suggested Answers

A boy was stuck on a cliff.
A helicopter came to rescue him.
The man in the helicopter got ready to get the boy.
The man was lowered down to the boy.
The man picked up the boy, and they were winched back up to the helicopter.
The boy's parents were pleased to see their son safe again.

Encourage your child to make up short captions for pictures in comics.

page 25 Answers

13, 10, 17
16, 14, 17
Check your child's numbers add up to the total in the middle.

When adding three numbers, look for pairs of easier numbers to add and then add the third number.

P26&27 Sandcastles

page 26 Suggested Answers

sand: band, hand, land, grand, stand, bland
shell: bell, fell, sell, tell, well, yell
net: bet, get, jet, let, met, pet, set, wet, yet
hat: bat, cat, fat, mat, pat, rat, sat, chat

Rhyming is a very useful spelling skill. Have rhyming competitions with your child.

page 27 Answers

1.   11, 10, 9, 13
2.   10 + 6 = 16, 8 + 8 = 16

It is important for your child to know all the number bonds for the numbers up to 10.

P28&29 Holiday snaps

page 28 Suggested Answers

On Tuesday I made sandcastles.
On Wednesday it rained.
On Thursday I went to the seaside.
On Friday I went on the Big Dipper.

Encourage your child to make up short captions for your holiday photos.

page 29 Answers

Check your child's answers.

Make sure your child draws the hour hand shorter than the minute hand. Look at clocks throughout the day and ask 'What time shall we have dinner?' or 'What time does the shop close?'

Draw your own face on this picture.

Ex-shell-ent!